Take me out to the Ball game

Maryann Kovalski

SCHOLASTIC INC.

New York   Toronto   London   Auckland   Sydney

Jenny and Joanna were baseball mad.

"Play ball!" they would call to anyone they could find.

Fly balls, grounders. Pitch, hit, slide. "You're out!"
Then, "One more game!" they'd shout.

Only one call could make a game stall
and Grandma's came one day —

6

"I'd like to know where you want to go?"
And snap! like that they sang . . .

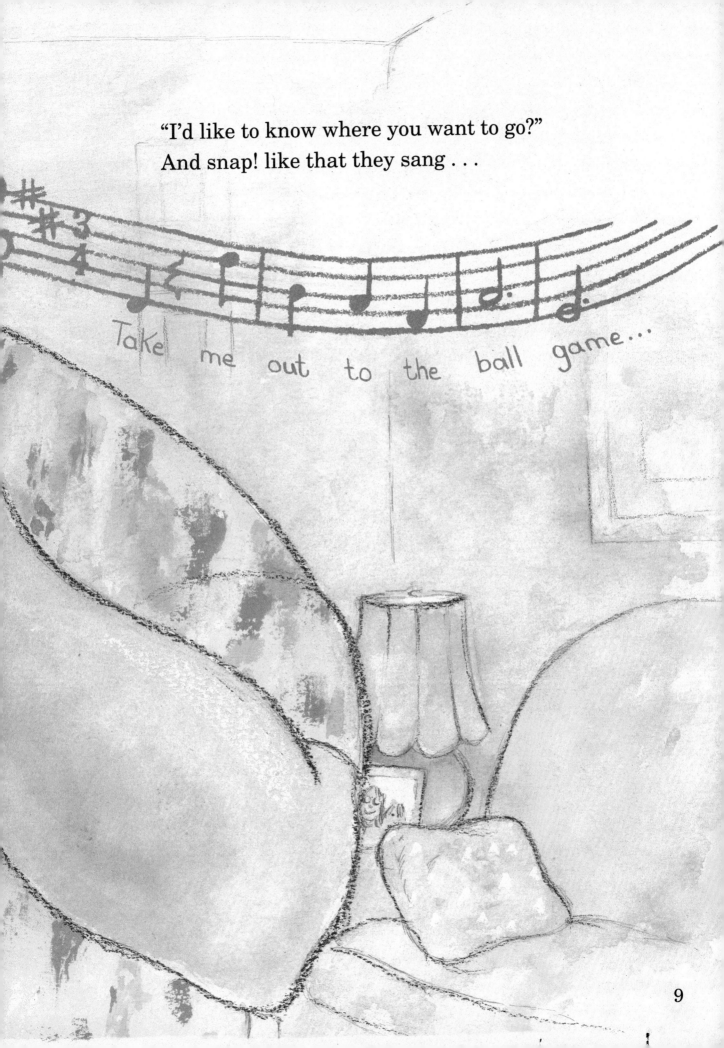

Take me out to the ball game...

Take me out to the ball game,

take me out to the crowd!

Buy me some peanuts and Cracker Jack,

I don't care if I never get back!

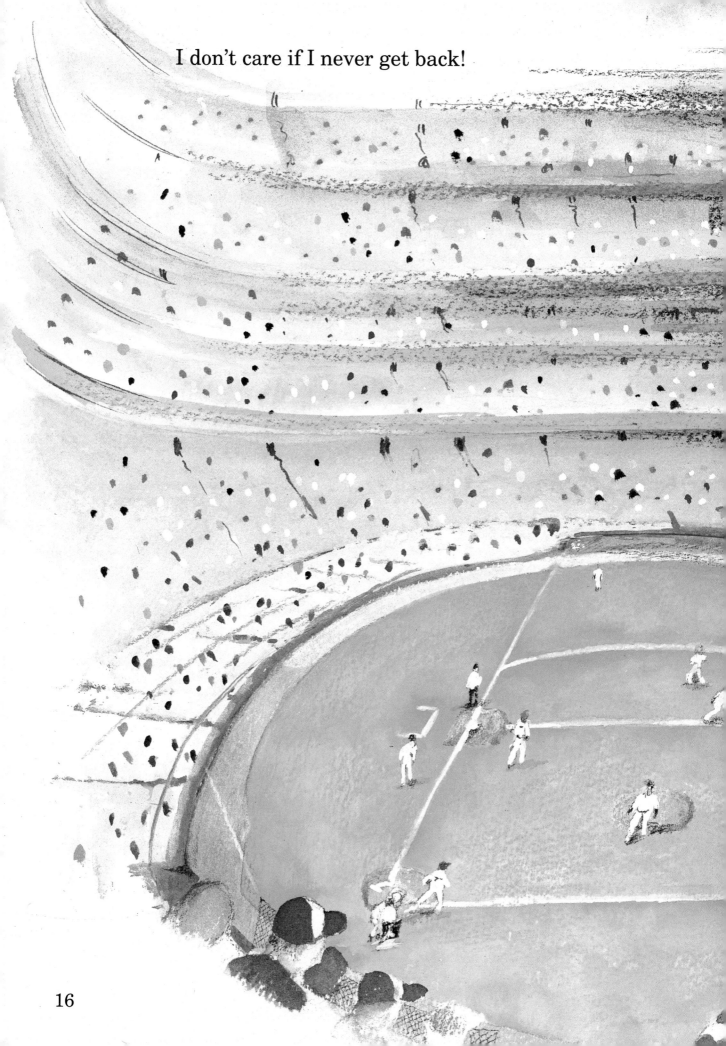

Let me root, root, root for the home team,

...if they don't win it's a shame!

For it's one . . .

two . . .

three strikes —

"You're out!"

At the old ball game!

Take Me Out to the Ball Game

Words by Jack Norworth

Music by Albert von Tilzer

Take me out to the ball game,

Take me out to the crowd._____

Buy me some pea - nuts and crack - er jack

I don't care if I nev- er come back, Let me

root, root, root for the home team, If

they don't win it's a shame._____ For it's

one, two, three strikes, "You're out!" at the

old ball game._____

For Gail

ISBN 0-590-45639-3

Copyright © 1992 by Maryann Kovalski.
All rights reserved. Published by Scholastic Inc.,
730 Broadway, New York, NY 10003 by arrangement with
North Winds Press, an imprint of Scholastic Canada Limited.

12 11 10 9 8 7 6 5 4 3 2 1   5   3 4 5 6 7 8/9

Printed in the U.S.A.   08